Norma Chapma

Fallow deer

Anthony Nelson

First published in 1984 by Anthony Nelson Ltd
PO Box 9, Oswestry, Shropshire SY11 1BY, England.

Series editor Robert Burton
Drawings by Jean Vaughan and Graham Allen
Photographs by Norma Chapman, John Fawcett, Peter Gasson,
Stephen Harris, Geoffrey Kinns, Pat Morris, P. Valentin-Jensen,
Roy Worsfold

Royalties from this series will go to the Mammal Society

British Library Cataloguing in Publication Data

Chapman, Norma
Fallow deer.—(Mammal Society booklets)
1. Red deer—Juvenile literature   2. Mammals
—Great Britain—Juvenile literature
I. Title   II. Series
599.73'57   QL737.U55

ISBN 0 904614 14 X

Designed by Alan Bartram
Printed by Livesey Ltd, 7 St John's Hill, Shrewsbury

Inside front cover
Bucks and does in Richmond Park.
*The top picture shows the 'browse line', with all tree growth cropped below
a certain height.*
Bottom, bucks sparring.

To many people the fallow deer is our most attractive deer, and for this reason it is kept in many parks. So there is plenty of opportunity of observing these lovely creatures, even if they cannot be seen in the countryside.

Deer have the rare distinction of having a nationally known traffic warning sign, illustrated in our *Highway Code*. In many counties where this sign is erected, the fallow deer is the most likely species to be encountered by a motorist, for it is the most widespread of the seven species of free-living deer in Britain. In towns and villages all over England signs of deer can be seen hanging outside public houses, for the White Hart (the badge of Richard II, a popular monarch) surely must be the commonest mammal name for an inn. In many cases the animal shown is a white fallow buck although in some instances a white red deer stag is shown, a hart originally being the term for a six year old red deer stag.

The fallow deer is a member of the deer family Cervidae. To distinguish our fallow deer from its close relation the Persian fallow deer, its full name is the European fallow deer (*Dama dama dama*). The Persian or Mesopotamian fallow deer (*Dama dama mesopotamica*) is endangered, and indeed it is doubtful whether it still survives in the wild in Iran, its last refuge. Apart from being larger, the body is very like the common-coloured European fallow deer, but the form of the antlers is different. The two subspecies have bred in captivity and the offspring are fertile.

The fallow deer is especially interesting for several reasons. Despite its widespread distribution and large size, keen fieldcraft is needed to observe it in the wild because its acute senses and wariness give it the seemingly magic property of being able to melt into its background. The reward for mastering

3

the skills of fieldcraft are delightful, although sometimes tantalising, hours spent watching the deer going about their everyday living. I was introduced to these joys by my late husband, Donald, in the 1960s when he began to investigate the natural history and biology of fallow deer, about which so little was then known. Despite all the hours spent in fieldwork and laboratory studies since those days, the thrill of hearing clashing antlers or the sight of a young fawn has never waned.

Appearance

The fallow deer is the second largest native land mammal in Britain, after the red deer. (The small herd of reindeer in the Cairngorms were brought from Sweden in 1952). An adult buck (the male) may weigh 45–95 kilograms but most does (the females) fall within the range 35–55 kilograms. At the shoulder a mature buck stands about 90 centimetres tall whereas a doe is shorter. Weights and measurements will vary according to the age of the animal and the quantity and quality of food available.

Fallow deer and reindeer differ from the other deer because they occur in a number of colour varieties. The common ones are 'common-colour', menil, black, and white. The colour varieties in fallow deer are associated with their long history of semi-domestication in parks. They are similar to the different colours of cattle, dogs and cats and, as in these animals, colour varieties of fallow deer can interbreed.

The typical colouring of fallow deer is called common-colour. In summer, this coat has a deep, rich, chestnut-brown background with many white spots over the back and flanks and a black line along the middle of the back. In autumn, it is gradually moulted to a duller, greyer brown, usually with no spots or only a trace of a few pale, indistinct ones. This coat is retained until the following spring when the deer passes through a scruffy phase as the brighter summer coat replaces it. All through the year the rump is white with a black curved border and the tail is white with a central black stripe, so that the deer looks as if the number 111 is painted on its rump.

The menil variety is similar to the common-colour variety, but the background brown is paler, the black lines are replaced by brown, the spots are more obvious in summer and they are retained in winter although fewer, paler and less distinct. In both these colour varieties the lower flank and belly is white in summer and off-white in winter. Between these two distinct forms there are some intermediate colour variations.

The black variety has no white at all. In summer the coat is glossy black with slight dappling of dark brown spots, often showing more on the neck than elsewhere. In winter the sheen is lost and the colour is duller, almost chocolate-brown and the belly is grey rather than the mushroom in summer. The rump and tail are black but the terminal hairs of the tail, which make the tail about 30 centimetres long, are often copper colour.

The fourth of the regularly occurring colour varieties is the white fallow deer. This is not a true albino because the eye colour is normal. However, it does lack some of the pigments that give the other varieties black noses and hooves, so it does have paler, rather orange hooves and nose. At birth, the fawns are a sandy colour and gradually acquire an off-white coat, usually after several moults.

A rare variation occurs in some of the deer in just one locality, Mortimer Forest in Shropshire. This concerns the length of the hairs, not their colour. The whole coat has unusually long hairs and 'curls' hang from the base of the ears and forehead.

Except in white fallow deer, the newly born fawns have coats like the summer coats of the adults. This is not necessarily the same as the colour of either parent.

Coat colours are alike in bucks and does but there are secondary sexual characteristics which distinguish them while they are still young. In the bucks, the Adam's apple (voice box) in the throat is very prominent. More distinctive still is the brush of hairs that hangs from the penis sheath. In the females, there is a slimmer tassel of long hairs hanging below the vulva. However, a buck's main distinction is his crowning glory, his antlers, which are described below.

A few moments' observation of a deer can tell us much about its life-style. The long legs suggest it is fleet of foot. Close examination of the feet show that the deer walks on cloven hooves which represent just two of the five toes of ancestral mammals. The remnants of two more toes are seen as tiny hoof-like dew claws, just above the back of the hooves. The lightness and slender structure of the lower leg is achieved by the heavy muscles which work the leg being bunched in the upper part and attached to the bones of the lower leg by long tendons.

Watch a deer grazing and notice how, while its mouth is down, plucking grass, its eyes are scanning the surrounding area. They are on the side of its head so it can see through a very wide angle. Your slightest movement is usually detected. If a strange object is placed in a deer's familiar area it will spend some time peering, with the neck outstretched as though to gain a better view. Should danger threaten, the deer will run to cover very swiftly. Or watch a deer that has been disturbed but not sufficiently alarmed to run. See how it sniffs the air, or swivels its ears without having to make the more conspicuous movement of turning its body. Smell and hearing are vital senses to a wild mammal, but their importance is hard for us to appreciate.

Antlers

Antlers are the most exciting and fascinating feature of deer. They are altogether rather improbable structures, found in no other group of animals, and they frequently attain a magnificent size and shape. Above all, there is the curious fact that they are cast and regrown annually. No other mammalian appendage is capable of completely regrowing once, let alone every year. Antlers are made of bone only, and so are different from the horns of sheep and cattle. Only male deer have antlers, except for reindeer, and musk deer and Chinese water deer are the only species lacking antlers completely.

The story of a fallow deer antler begins when a male fawn is about six months old and a pair of small hair-covered bumps begins to grow on his head. These are the pedicles which will be permanent structures for the rest of his life and on these the antlers will grow. Soon the first signs of antlers will appear, at first hard to distinguish from the pedicles, because they, too, are covered with hairy skin. The hairs are short and erect so, because of its appearance and texture, the skin covering the new antlers is called velvet. Within the velvet there are blood vessels which carry oxygen and food to the bone of the growing antler.

Growth continues until about August, when the first pair of antlers usually have attained their full size. The function of the velvet is then complete and it is shed. The antlers are now described as clean and hard. The young male, called a pricket when he has acquired his first set of antlers, encourages removal of the velvet by rubbing or 'fraying' the antlers against vegetation.

Whether the first antlers are short and stubby or are slender spikes, perhaps 20 centimetres long, is likely to depend partly on the pricket's inherited characteristics and partly on the quality of food he has been eating. Although simple, unbranched first antlers are usual, occasionally the first set may have one or two branches, a fact only recently established.

The first set of antlers is retained until the following June when it is cast,

Development of a young buck's second head of antlers, from casting to shedding the velvet.

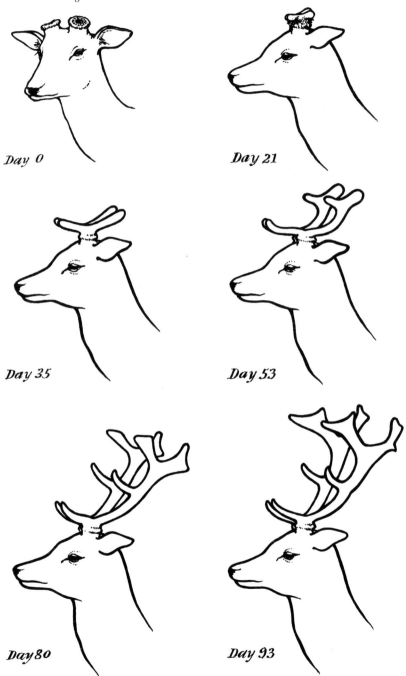

Day 0

Day 21

Day 35

Day 53

Day 80

Day 93

often with a day or so interval between the two halves. There is some bleeding from the top of the pedicle but a scab soon forms and remains obvious for some days. It is surrounded by a rim of new growth, the beginnings of the next antler. Seen close-to, the appearance is rather like two strawberry jam tarts, with dry jam and rather pale pastry, stuck on the animal's head. The antler continues to grow and rapidly changes from a velvet-covered ring to a dome which then begins to lengthen.

The second set of antlers have forward-projecting points or tines which branch from the beam, or main stem. The form of the second antler, and indeed later ones, is very variable, even among bucks living in the same area. Some have slight flattening of the beam at its distal end. This is the beginning of 'palmation', the broadening of the antler into a 'palm' which is characteristic of older fallow bucks and makes their antlers quite unlike those of any other deer in Britain. Growth of these antlers continues until August when the velvet is shed, often hanging in tatters for a day or so until the buck has rubbed it off. This pair, called the second head, is retained until the following May, when the cycle begins all over again.

The early morning walker or horse-rider in a park may be lucky enough to find a newly cast antler, but if it is not found soon it will become covered by vegetation or gnawed by squirrels or other rodents. Some enthusiasts even watch a particular half-cast buck all day, eagerly hoping to see the second antler drop. In the wild, the finding of an antler is an even more thrilling experience.

In general a fallow buck's antlers increase in size in successive years until he is past his prime, but his age cannot be determined from the appearance of the antlers, as the illustrations show.

Antlers are weapons and status symbols. Males can assess each others' ages and social standing peacefully. Only when rival bucks are very evenly matched is a conflict likely to ensue, with clashing of antlers and much shoving. Quite serious fights can occur in the mating season, and parts of antlers are fairly often broken, but this causes no pain because the antler is dead bone. Occasionally, instead of there being a winner and the loser who retreats, both bucks die a lingering death because their antlers have become inextricably interlocked. One deer park keeper, seeing two of his finest bucks entangled, was able to skilfully shoot away a portion of antler, so that the bucks could disengage and live to fight another day.

History and distribution

In Britain, the fallow deer became extinct before the end of the last Ice Age. Fine examples of the antlers of the very large Clacton fallow deer (*Dama dama clactoniana*) can be seen in the British Museum (Natural History) in London. They date from 250,000 years ago. Smaller in size but still larger than the present-day animals was the fallow deer from 100,000 years ago, first found in

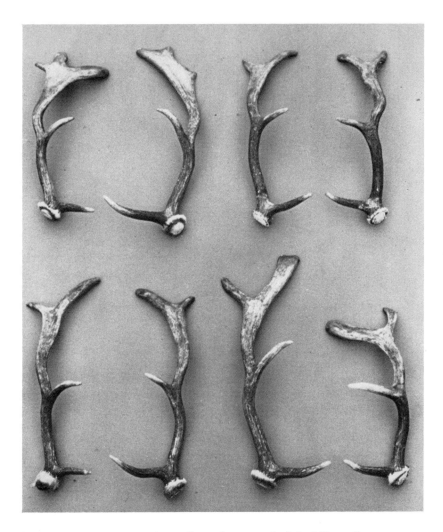

Devon. Visitors are sometimes allowed to enter the Joint Mitnor Cave at Buckfastleigh, a treasure chest crammed with various animal bones where the fallow deer bones were first discovered.

The reason for the fallow deer's present wide distribution in Britain lies in its long history as a park animal and as a quarry for hunting. It was almost certainly brought to England by the Normans in the eleventh century and established in forests as a royal beast of the chase. Some of the remnants of our ancient deciduous forests have held wild fallow deer for centuries, back to the times when they were the monarch's quarry. A few of the hunting lodges used

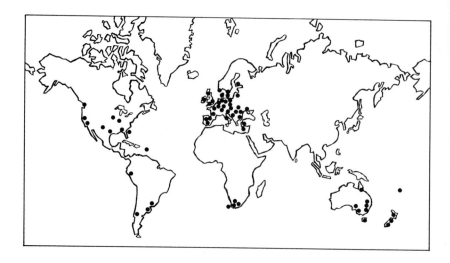

on hunts still exist. Queen Elizabeth's Hunting Lodge, at Chingford in Epping Forest, only 16 kilometres from central London, is a fine example which now serves as a museum.

Later, herds of fallow deer became a choice ornament when country gentlemen landscaped their parks. To prevent the deer coming into the flower gardens and lawns around the house, a ha-ha was constructed to keep the deer out. A ha-ha is a brick wall forming one side of a moat-like ditch, sometimes 2.5 metres deep, to make a deer-proof barrier which cannot be seen from the house. Many ha-has can still be seen around country houses although there are no longer any deer to keep out.

In the present century, two World Wars have resulted in the disappearance of deer parks. There was a shortage of man-power and materials to repair fences, and sometimes the parkland was ploughed following the shooting of the deer. Dispersal over the fences or mass escapes through broken fences was assisted by troops assembled nearby. From these escapes many populations of completely free-living deer have become established, and most wild populations can be traced to a particular park herd. The growth of Forestry Commission plantations since 1919 has provided many new habitats for the escaped deer.

The present world-wide distribution of fallow deer bears no relationship to its original distribution. The area around the Mediterranean and Asia Minor must have been the original home of the fallow deer, but the only place where it still occurs naturally there is in Turkey, where small numbers survive. However, because of the fallow deer's attractive appearance, the excellence of its meat and, in some cases, its suitability for sport shooting, it has been introduced throughout the world, from Finland to New Zealand, from Fiji to three islands in the Gulf of Vancouver.

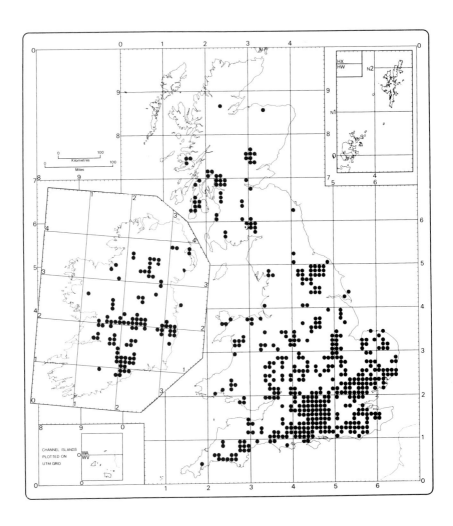

Habitat

The typical habitat of fallow deer is deciduous woodland, often with arable land or pasture in the vicinity. However, the deer frequently occur in predominantly coniferous woodland, which usually have some belts of broad-leaved trees and wide grass rides. They can also survive in quite a wide

11

range of other habitats, as shown when they have been introduced to an alien environment in other continents, and extensive areas of forest are not essential. A series of small woods interspersed with farmland is often the habitat used. When they feed in open fields, meadows or heaths, fallow deer like to be close to woodland where they can flee for safety if danger threatens. Fallow deer occur in the same woodland as other species of deer, frequently the Chinese muntjac, often the roe deer and sometimes red deer. The New Forest probably has the record for the number of species in one forest, as fallow, roe, sika, red and muntjac all occur there. The Bolderwood Sanctuary within that Forest, near Lyndhurst, provides an opportunity for visitors to see fallow deer at close quarters.

Food

Although fallow deer are predominantly grazing animals and feed on grass and herbs, they also browse on the taller vegetation of shrubs and trees, taking whatever is palatable and within reach, standing on their hind limbs to reach if necessary and thus creating a distinct browse line.

As well as eating grasses, various herbs growing amongst them will be taken. Most species of broad-leaved trees are eaten, particularly in the spring when the leaves are young and tender, but hornbeam and sycamore are ignored. Even tough holly leaves may be eaten. The autumn crop of acorns, horse and sweet chestnuts and beech mast are eaten with relish and provide a major source of autumn and winter food in a good nut year. Other fruits such as hips, haws and blackberries are taken, and fungi also feature in the diet. Conifer leaves are eaten but Corsican pine is ignored. Bramble and ivy are favourite foods in any season. Heather contributes importantly to the diet where it is available and tree bark may be stripped in winter. If crops of carrots, potatoes or sugar beet are available, fallow deer are sure to sample them and rural gardens are not exempt from their attention: rose bushes, peas and parsnips are all particularly favoured. Cereal crops will also attract their interest. In the early stages of short growth, grazing may stimulate greater tillering (putting out extra shoots) and so actually improve the crop.

Leaves are bitten off by the chisel-like front teeth of the lower jaws which bite against the hard fibrous pad of tissue at the front of the upper jaw, where there are no teeth. There is a large gap behind the lower front teeth and the cheek teeth, which, in a fallow deer older than about 26 months, consist of three premolars and three molars, on each side, top and bottom. These cheek teeth are typical for herbivorous mammals, which move their jaws from side to side when chewing. They have ridges, running parallel with the length of jaw, which make an efficient grinding surface. The ridges become worn down and smoother with age and in old deer the crowns of the teeth will be almost flat, and may be broken or lost.

Once bitten off, the food is chewed only partially and is swallowed quickly.

The stomach is a large organ in deer and other cud-chewing animals like sheep and cattle, and consists of four distinct chambers. The herbage enters the first two chambers: the bag-like rumen and the much smaller reticulum, where it is stored. When the deer has eaten its fill, it begins to chew the cud, or ruminate, often after retreating to a sheltered spot. A ball of food is regurgitated into the mouth – you can see this happening if you are near the deer and can see its throat clearly. Then after a thorough grinding by the teeth, it is swallowed again and returned to the stomach, this time entering the third chamber, called the omasum. Here, the particles of food are ground between the leaf-like folds of the lining before passing into the remaining chamber, the true stomach. Gastric juices are mixed with the food there before it passes into the intestine to be finally digested and absorbed.

Breeding

The mating season in October and November is known as the rut. The bucks concentrate a great deal of activity into these few weeks. They eat hardly anything but use so much energy that, by the end of the rut, they look worn-out. One buck found lying in bracken was so exhausted that he was believed to be dead until he was approached to within a couple of metres.

Typical activities of the rut are scraping, thrashing and fraying. Scrapes are made with the hooves of the forelegs among the dead leaves and soil of the woodland floor or amongst grass. They are normally shallow depressions, very variable in size, but most have a diameter between 0.3 metres and 2 metres. Into some of these the buck urinates, leaving the unmistakable, pungent rutty odour so characteristic of bucks at this season. At this time the hairs of his brush are stained and splayed out, the end of his penis sheath has everted and looks like dry, heat-cracked soil and a scent gland is active there. His belly also becomes stained.

With his antlers, a buck thrashes hawthorn bushes, elder saplings or whatever low woody vegetation is available, some branches being snapped off completely. Sometimes the same shrubs, but also additional ones, have their bark stripped bare or frayed, for perhaps 50 centimetres, on one side of the stem. Pliant young woody stems are the victims of this fraying. Deeper, gouged grooves may be made in the bark of thicker trunks. Although most conspicuous when freshly inflicted, these wounds remain, with the edges of the bark healed, for the life of the tree. They can be found at any time of year and indicate where deer rutting takes place. (It must be remembered that the males of other deer cause similar damage.)

The circumference of a buck's neck increases greatly for the rut. His Adam's apple is even more prominent than usual and he makes a deep, belching groan. This eerie sound carries far on a cold crisp night or frosty dawn but may also be heard during the day. Bucks may use their groans as a means of assessing each other's status, before deciding whether or not to engage in battle as has been shown with red deer stags. If two bucks are prepared to fight, they walk parallel to each other before turning face to face, unless one decides not to press his case any further and flees.

The bucks keep watch over a group of does who have their well-grown fawns with them. As each doe comes into season the buck will mount her, after much preliminary chivvying, sniffing and licking of her rear end. During this activity a buck will exhibit *flehmen* – a German word, for which there is no equivalent in English, to describe the curled-back lips, the tilted nose and outstretched neck as the buck savours the smell and taste of the doe's urine. The youngest females to be mated will be 16 months old. Males of this age are fertile but in the wild would rarely have the opportunity to mate because of their low rank in the male hierarchy. They can be seen waiting on the periphery of a rutting area, probably looking for a chance to sneak in if the buck moves away.

These activities are typical of the fallow rut but there is quite a range in the pattern of the rutting behaviour in the wild and in parks. In some localities the same rutting areas are used year after year, the bucks returning to a traditional piece of ground – the rutting stand – from where much groaning is heard and around which a group of does assembles. Elsewhere, the same areas within a wood are not used in successive years, but the behaviour pattern is otherwise

similar. Whereas groaning is a conspicuous sign of the rut being in full swing in many areas, elsewhere little is heard although the following year's crop of fawns proves that the rut took place. In some parks one or two bucks gain a monopoly of most of the does, whereas elsewhere most mature bucks will hold at least some females. Yet another and spectacular rut pattern occurs in a few extensive parks when a large number of mature bucks assemble together and parade as though in an arena.

Whatever form the rut takes, seven months later the fawns are born. A single fawn is the rule. The only proven live birth of twins was in an enclosure in the United States, although twin foetuses have been found in a very small number of does shot or accidentally killed in Britain.

Although the majority of fawns are born in mid-June, a few later births occur, even as late as October or November, showing that the doe did not conceive successfully in the rutting season but was covered by a buck when she came into season again later.

At birth an average fawn weighs 4.5 kilograms. Although capable of tottering after its dam within a few hours of birth, generally the fawn will be left to lie for the first few days concealed in bracken, long grass, stinging nettles or other vegetation, or just on leaf litter where its dappled coat camouflages it. The exquisite beauty of a newly born fawn lying alone, looking so appealing and helpless, has led to tragedy for many. People do not appreciate that it is normal for a young fawn to be alone while its mother goes to feed, often at a considerable distance away, so they 'rescue' it. At any season of year, a deer must spend much time in feeding, and this especially applies when a doe has to maintain herself and provide milk for her baby. At intervals during the day she returns to suckle her fawn, but she will not do so if humans are near. A fawn lying alone is not abandoned, but merely resting between meals.

While suckling her fawn, which stands diagonally to the udder, the doe licks its rear. This not only keeps the fawn's anal area clean but also stimulates defæcation. The mother grooms other parts of the body but the fawn starts to groom itself at a very early age.

Initially the doe's milk is the fawn's only food but soon tiny pieces of leaves will be eaten. As the fawn grows and gains in strength, and eats more vegetation, it spends more time following at the heels of its mother. By the time it is a month or two old it plays with its contemporaries, apparently playing games akin to tag and jumping on and off small mounds. Later they take part in vigorous playful chases in circles, often round a pond or a stump or other central feature.

Herbage becomes the major part of the diet although some milk may be taken at least to the end of the year, and some does are still lactating even into January or February. The close season for female fallow deer, when it is illegal to shoot them except under certain circumstances, is March 1–October 31 in England and Wales but February 16–October 20 in Scotland. These seasons prevent young, fully dependent fawns being orphaned by stalkers.

Social behaviour

Fallow deer are gregarious animals; they are often seen together in large herds, particularly as the rut approaches, or if disturbance, such as a fox-hunt, has flushed them from woods into the open fields. However, single animals or small groups are often encountered, although the same animals may later congregate in larger herds in favourable feeding areas. If a large herd is disturbed, the deer may run off in a group before splitting into smaller parties which may not be the same as those that had come together to form the large herd in the first place only an hour earlier. For much of the year these small groups consist of does with their fawns and young males. In some areas at least, males remain with the doe groups until they are about 18 months old and lone prickets may then be encountered, before they join the all-male groups.

The size of the area over which a deer ranges in its day-to-day activities is likely to vary according to the quality of the habitat and the amount of disturbance. Within this area the deer must be able to find adequate food at all seasons of the year, and it must also have shelter from chilling winds and sufficient cover to hide in. For fallow does living in deciduous woodland and arable fields in Essex this area is around 40 hectares. This was found by studying individually recognisable animals which had been caught and given ear-tags. Fallow bucks have two home ranges, spending different parts of the year in different areas, perhaps some kilometres apart. In the early autumn they join the does in preparation for the breeding season. After this, either straight away or a month or so later, they return to their non-breeding ranges, where they remain in buck groups away from the does until the following autumn.

Sounds and scents

A buck's rutting groans are loud and unmistakable but outside the breeding

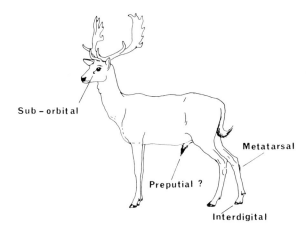

Sub – orbital

Metatarsal

Preputial ?

Interdigital

season he makes little sound. During the rut the does make whickering noises but for the rest of the year their most usual noise is a short, sharp bark, uttered several times when they are alarmed or suspicious, often when a concealed fawn is in the vicinity. While the fawns are young they mew and the mother bleats.

A deer's habitat is no doubt strewn with information meaningful to the deer but not understood or even detected by man, for his sense of smell is poorly developed. Scent glands are important means of communication in many mammals but the deer family is especially well-endowed. On the head, fallow deer have a pair of scent glands, situated just below the corner of each eye. These consist of pockets of skin which fit into depressions in the skull immediately next to the eye sockets. The pocket lining secretes a brown, waxy substance. When closed the pocket shows as a short curved line in the fur below the eye but on various occasions it is opened. During courtship a buck will open these glands and wipe them against a doe's flank.

Between the cleaves (the two toes) of each hind foot lies another, deeper pocket in the skin. This, too, is lined with secretory cells which produce a yellow creamy substance smelling like rancid-butter and which is presumably deposited on the ground as the deer walks or runs. Yet another scent gland is located in a much more conspicuous place, on the hock. Its position shows clearly as a raised pad of hairs on the outer side of the hind leg.

Parasites and diseases

Wild fallow deer are generally very healthy and free from disease. Although they can be infected by a wide range of bacterial and viral diseases, such cases are rare, and there are a few records of tumours in some organs, such as the liver.

Fallow deer can be hosts to various ectoparasites but the incidence varies in different localities. In Essex, ticks are rarely seen on fallow deer, whereas in West Suffolk they are common, because the sheep tick, which sucks blood from many hosts, is abundant in the region. Lice are seldom present in large numbers, except on poor-doers debilitated by lack of food in bad weather or loss of the mother at an early age, but a few lice may be found, most often in the groin where they feed on skin debris.

Keds are blood-sucking, strange-looking flies which are wingless for much of the year. Their body, flattened from above to below, is perfectly adapted for scuttling with a crab-like sideways movement among the hairs of the coat of the deer.

Internal worms in the gut are few in numbers and cause the deer no problems. Similarly, the incidence of round worms in the lungs is low. Liverfluke is rare and bladder worms, the larval stage of a tapeworm, are most likely to be found in fallow deer where dogs or foxes have access to the deer's pasture.

Signs

Wherever there are fallow deer there are tell-tale signs of their presence. They can jump a barrier with ease but usually prefer to duck under a strand of wire in a fence or push through a gap in a hedge, and sometimes leave a tuft of hairs on a barb or thorn. Where the ground is suitable, footprints will be made, but caution must be exercised in identifying the species that made them. All deer have slender, cloven feet and leave similarly shaped tracks whose size will vary with age and sex within a species as well as among species. Tracks often show best at a crossing place by a hedge, fence, bank or ditch and often lead the observer to a well-worn path, for deer are creatures of habit, using the same route time and time again.

Identifying the droppings made by different species of deer is also difficult. Again, there are close similarities among the species and size alone is not totally reliable, especially if one has, for example, immature red deer and adult fallow deer in one area. The droppings are firm, black, cylindrical pellets. They do not look fibrous like rabbit and hare droppings but are glossy when fresh. The typical size of a single pellet for an adult doe is 15 × 8 millimetres; bucks produce larger pellets. A heap of perhaps 25–100 pellets is deposited at a time, often by a lying-up place but anywhere within the deer's range.

In autumn there will be many additional fresh signs of activities in the breeding areas (see *Breeding*).

Relations with Man

The interests of man and fallow deer impinge on each other more today than ever before. Probably the fallow deer is now more numerous than at any time

for centuries and Man is virtually its only predator. At the same time farmers want the maximum yield from agricultural land, and excessive damage to trees will not be tolerated by foresters.

More highways than ever before cut across the land, carrying more and faster vehicles. Human fatalities in road traffic accidents involving deer are fortunately very rare but damage to cars is not uncommon. The consequences of a vehicle hitting a deer on a multi-lane motorway could be horrific, so very expensive preventative measures have to be implemented in areas of high deer density. Motorists on some lengths of road, such as the M11 in Essex, will notice many kilometres of 2 metre-high chain-link fencing to prevent deer straying onto the road, but even this does not eliminate all deer accidents.

Long lengths of road in many counties are lined by posts bearing reflective plates. First erected at deer accident black-spots, the earliest type were small, square shiny metal plates designed to reflect the beams of headlights back into the wood and so deter the deer from crossing. A more recent development has been a reflecting plate, mounted on a short post. When a beam from a vehicle's lights strikes the plate, a wall of red light shows up, apparently seen by animals but not by man. However, to be effective in practice, the reflectors need cleaning and maintenance, and they do not function in fog.

In many areas, road accidents are the most likely cause of a deer not reaching old age. The number of fallow deer killed on roads each year is unknown and certainly many others receive injuries from which they die later or sustain broken bones which may heal. In captivity fallow deer may live for over 20 years but in parks, where annual culling is carried out to maintain the

numbers at a manageable level, they would normally be shot long before this age.

Hazards which can have indirect, fatal results are all too frequently left about the countryside. Tough, coloured plastic string for binding bales of hay and straw is frequently discarded on farms or in stable yards. Fallow deer are inquisitive animals, not averse to nosing and probing in rubbish heaps, and in this way a number of unfortunate bucks have acquired a head-dress of string. This in itself may not be too bothersome, but one buck got a length of the dangling string caught between the cleaves of one forefoot also, thus restricting movements of his head and leg which could never be more than the string's length apart. Two fairly young bucks were found dead, with their antlers interlocked not by the tines of their fairly simple antlers, but by a mass of string enmeshing the tines of the antlers. Each had taken some days to die a miserable death.

Deer in public parks are particularly exposed to a further menace, namely discarded polythene bags, especially if they develop the habit of scavenging from litter bins. The polythene cannot be digested so remains in the stomach, somewhat chewed, and becomes twisted into a 'rope' or ball. As certain individuals become regular scroungers, a large number of polythene bags and miscellaneous other items of rubbish can accumulate in one stomach, with the ultimate risk of blockage.

Whereas semi-domestication of deer in parks has continued for centuries, only in the last decade has deer-farming become established, first with red deer and then with fallow deer. They are farmed, often on a large scale, in various countries including New Zealand, Australia, West Germany, Denmark, as well as England. Although the value of venison, skins and antlers have long been appreciated, as have the tail hairs for tying fishing flies, in recent years other parts of the carcase, such as the testes, penis and leg sinews, which were previously discarded, have found a profitable outlet in Asian markets.

The opportunities of deer parks

The presence of deer in many parks, some close to large towns, makes deer-watching a possibility for many people who do not have the opportunity of finding and watching wild deer. Because the deer in public parks are used to people, you can get relatively close and observe quite well, even without binoculars.

Whatever the season there is something special to look for. While the rut in autumn provides the most exciting highlight of the year, the most charming sights will be those of young fawns playing or following their mothers in early summer. Observations during antler casting and velvet shedding can produce an interesting series of photographs, sketches or a series of dates which can be compared from year to year. Changes in the social groupings of the deer during the year can be observed, for even in a park where the bucks cannot move to a different locality after the rut, they still set up separate groups apart from the does and fawns.

If a particular buck can be identified reliably, the growth of a set of antlers can be followed over frequent visits. Observing the progress of a moult, which would not be possible in the wild, is another possibility. Much can be learned from observing a park herd, and the practice should not be despised for being too easy.

Deer parks open to the public

Avon
1. *Ashton Court Park, Bristol*
2. *Dyrham Park, Chippenham*

Bedfordshire
3. *Woburn Park, Woburn Sands*
4. *Whipsnade Park, Dunstable*

Cheshire
5. *Lyme Park, Disley*
6. *Tatton Park, Knutsford*

Cumbria
7. *Holker Hall, Cark-in-Cartmel*
8. *Levens Hall Park, Kendal*

Derbyshire
9. *Chatsworth Park, Bakewell*

Essex
10. *St Osyth Priory, Colchester*

Gloucestershire
11. *Lydney Park, Chepstow*

Greater London
12. *Bushey Park and Hampton Park*
13. *Greenwich Park*
14. *Maryon Wilson Park, Charlton*
15. *Clissold Park, N16*
16. *Golders Hill Park*
17. *Victoria Park*

Greater Manchester
18. *Dunham Massey Park, Altrincham*

Hereford and Worcester
19. *Eastnor Castle Park, Ledbury*
20. *Spetchely Park, Worcester*

Hertfordshire
21. *Knebworth Park, Stevenage*

Kent
22. *Boughton Monchelsea Place, Maidstone*
23. *Knole Park, Sevenoaks*

Leicestershire
24. *Bradgate Park, Newtown Linford*

Lincolnshire
25. *Normanby Park, Scunthorpe*

Norfolk
26. *Houghton Hall Park, Fakenham*
27. *Holkham Park, Wells-next-the-Sea*

Nottinghamshire
28. *Wollaton Park, Nottingham*
29. *Thoresby Park, Newark*

Oxfordshire
30. *Magdalen College Park, Oxford*
31. *Stonor Park, Henley-on-Thames*

Shropshire
32. *Attingham Park, Shrewsbury*
33. *Weston Park, Shifnal*

Somerset
34. *Combe Sydenham Park, Watchet*
35. *Hatch Court Park, Hatch Beauchamp*

Suffolk
36. *Helmingham Hall, Stowmarket*

Surrey
37. *Richmond Park, Richmond*

Sussex
38. *Petworth Park, Midhurst*

Warwickshire
39. *Charlecote Park, Wellesbourne*

Yorkshire
40. *Studley Royal Park, Ripon*

Wales
41. *Margam Castle Park, Port Talbot*

Scotland
42. *Hopetoun House Park, Edinburgh*
43. *Kinnaird Castle, Brechin*

Ireland
44. *Lough Key Forest Park, Co Roscommon*
45. *Randalstown Forest Nature Reserve, Co Antrim*
46. *Phoenix Park, Dublin*

In the Chiltern beechwoods.

Opposite
Bucks and does, Richmond Park.
1. Buck in autumn.
2. Frayed sapling.
3 & 4 The dappled coats of fallow fawn (3) and red deer calf (4) make them easy to confuse.